Mint Tea

Patience, Forgiveness, Ills of the Tounque, and Other Short Stories to Warm the Heart

Volume 6

BY IMAN ABDALLAH AL-QAISI

Illustrator
Nadia Yousef

Translator
Maha Ezzeddine

Copy Editor
Sumaiya Susan Gavell
(Sterling International Editors)

Layout and Graphics
Zaid Al-Dabbagh
(Panda UX Studio Limited)

WEB APPS + UI/UX DESIGN + USABILITY/ACCESSIBILITY
WWW.PANDAUX.CO

Dedication and Introduction

All thanks and praise to God; I thank and praise You, my Dear Lord, first and foremost.

I then direct my gratitude to the orphans of the world: you have shone light upon my heart, inspiring in me a fervent dedication to your cause. By the will of God, your suffering has prompted the penning of words to make this a widely popular and best-selling series. To you I give special thanks and deference. And to you this project will forever be dedicated.

I would like to further recognize our volunteers, tireless soldiers who have expended sincere energy to produce this book.

Finally, with deep gratitude, I would like to thank the family of the late instructor Moazz Al-Qaisi, who sponsored the printing of this edition on their mother's behalf. I ask the All-Powerful Creator to grant her the mercy of the righteous, to resurrect her with the chosen select, and to permanently house her in a lofty abode in Paradise. May God accept her family's generous contribution and reward them abundantly. Ameen.

CONTENTS

"The one who cares for an orphan and myself will be like this in Heaven," as he held his index and middle fingers together.

Narrated by Bukhari

*   Abbreviation for "*salla Allahu alayhi wa sallam*," or "peace be upon him." Common Islamic etiquette dictates prayers of peace to be made for the Prophet Muhammad (s) at every written or spoken mention of his name.

— 1 —
The Orphan's Rank
Honor and Forgiveness

One day, the son of Caliph Umar ibn Abdul Aziz went hunting with his friend. During the outing, he quarrelled with his hunting companion, who happened to be an orphaned boy. Their heated exchange led to blows, and the orphan punched the son of the Caliph.

The wife of the Caliph was distraught when she saw blood pouring down her son's face. She was sure that her husband would deal with the reckless youth and punish him accordingly. The orphan youth was summoned before Umar ibn Abdul Aziz.

"Who are you, my son?" inquired the Caliph.

The boy gave his full name and then added, "My father was killed fighting for the sake of God."

"What a great family you come from!" exclaimed Umar. "Now, what do you think we should do with you?"

"Oh, Leader of the Believers," responded the boy, "I expect you will deal justly and give me what I deserve for unleashing my angry and hitting your son."

Umar turned thoughtfully to one of his scribes and asked, "Is this young man's name registered on the list of orphans in Muslim lands?" The scribe scanned the complete record of orphans and replied that he could not locate his name on the log.

"Then record his name and make sure he receives his full due from our treasury," said Umar. "We have committed enough injustice by forgetting about him after his father died."

When the wife of the Caliph heard that the boy who punched her son would be released without consequence, she voiced her concern to her husband.

Umar ibn Abdul Aziz answered her, "Remember the verse, 'to forgive is closer to God-consciousness.'" * And so the wife of the Caliph swallowed her frustration for the sake of her son in order to forgive for the sake of God. **

---

*   [Al-Baqarah:237]
**   From Dalil As-Sa'ileen by Anas Ismail Abu Dawud, p. 469.

Lessons Learned:

1. **Children of leaders should be raised righteously.**

   Too many famous and wealthy people raise children who grow up to be spoiled and undisciplined. When they are only acquainted with the richest tiers of society, they may live in privileged isolation and become disconnected with the needs, problems, and suffering of those less fortunate, those whom they may one day rule or employ. Few righteous rulers in history avoided this pitfall by making sure their children associated with people of all social and economic classes. Consequently, they raised children who were forgiving to those who wronged them. The Prophet (s) indicated that good character is not only the result of inborn traits, but can also be developed through practice: "Verily, knowledge comes about by striving for knowledge, and patience comes about by striving to be patient." * In order to be an effective leader in any field of life, leaders must be empathetic to those whom they will lead by remaining amongst them and being patient with their faults.

2. **God elevates those who fight for His sake.**

   The young man proudly identified himself as the son of a martyr who died in the cause of God. Caliph Umar acknowledged the child's lineage as noble, due to his father's sacrifice. Whereas orphaned children may sometimes feel grieved or abandoned, this boy was proud of his circumstances. God raises the rank of those who strive for His sake: "You who believe, shall I show you a bargain that will save you from painful torment? Have faith in God and His messenger and struggle for His cause with your possessions and your persons - that is better for you, if only you knew. And He will forgive your

---

*   Narrated by Tabari, *hasan* by Al-Albani.

sins, admit you into gardens graced with flowing streams, into pleasant dwellings in the Gardens of Eternity. That is the supreme triumph." *

3. **Assume the best of people.**

It takes a good deal of discipline and self-control to assume good of people, give excuses, and grant others the benefit of the doubt, especially when it does not seem warranted. When the young man was asked what he thought his punishment should be, the orphan showed his good character in admitting his fault and assuming that the Caliph would act justly. Similarly, Caliph Umar understood that the orphan acted impulsively and did not intend real harm. Both the young man and the Caliph upheld their character, and hence the outcome was fitting and beautiful. They avoided a grave mistake that God describes in the Quran, "Believers, avoid making too many assumptions - some assumptions are sinful." **

4. **Caring for orphans is worship.**

God commanded all people, especially those in positions of authority, to look after the needs of abandoned children. God says, "Remember when We took a pledge from the Children of Israel: 'Worship none but God; be good to your parents and kinsfolk, to orphans and the poor; speak good words to all people; keep up the prayer and pay the prescribed alms.' Then all but a few of you turned away and paid no heed." *** When Caliph Umar discovered that the state had not observed its responsibility in caring for the orphaned boy, he decided that the matter took priority over any other consideration. For this reason, he forgave the boy's transgression and immediately ordered that he should receive financial support for his father's

---

*   [As-Saff:10-12]
**   [Al-Hujurat:12]
***   [Al-Baqarah:83]

6

sacrifice. Meeting the needs of the weak, neglected, and orphaned is a practical form of worship that draws believers closer to God.

5. Forgiveness brings honor in this life and the next.

To forgive after being treated unjustly, as in this story, paves a path to God-consciousness. Umar intended a lesson for his wife and son; it was better for them to show forgiveness, even though they had been wronged, especially because they held positions of power. He modeled that forgiveness fosters love and elevates one to an honorable rank, in this life and the next. Prophet Muhammad (s) said, "Forgiveness only raises the honor of a servant, and the one who humbles himself for God, God will raise him high." [*]

[*] Narrated by Muslim.

"They ask you about orphans, say: 'It is good to set things right for them. If you combine their affairs with yours, remember they are your brothers and sisters; God knows those who spoil things and those who improve them. Had He so willed, He could have made you vulnerable too — He has the power to decide.'"

[Al-Baqarah:220]

— 2 —

A Wonderful Bargain

Giving for the Sake of God

During the lifetime of Prophet Muhammad (s), an orphaned boy from the city of Medina owned a grove of palm trees that adjoined a neighbor's garden. When the boy came of age, he decided to build a fence between his orchard and the neighboring plot of land. There was only one problem: a palm tree from the neighbor's garden grew in the way of the fence that the youth was planning to build.

The boy went to visit the owner of the neighboring garden.

"My brother," he said, "you have plenty of palm trees. Could you please give up just one palm tree that is blocking my fence?"

To the boy's surprise, the owner of the garden responded firmly, "No, by God, the tree is mine. I won't give it away."

"Would you consider selling it to me?" offered the young man. "I have money, and I am willing to buy it."

The owner of the garden was adamant: "I will never give up this tree!" he retorted.

The boy asked, "Could you please explain to me why this tree is so important? Its location is preventing me from building my fence."

"I'm sorry," said the neighbor, "but this is your problem, not mine."

So the orphan went to seek help directly from Prophet Muhammad (s), who was living in Medina at that time.

"Messenger of God," complained the boy, "my orchard lies next to the garden of one of my neighbors. I want to build a fence between our properties, but one of his trees is blocking the route. I have asked him to either give me the tree or sell it to me, but he has refused. Yet, I cannot build the fence unless we come to an agreement. Could you please persuade him to relinquish this tree?"

Prophet Muhammad (s) summoned the neighbor who owned the palm tree.

The Prophet verified the story, "Your garden lies next to this orphan's property, is that not so? And he would like to build a fence, but one of your trees is in the way."

The orphan's neighbor confirmed that the incident was true.

Prophet Muhammad (s) reasoned with the man and prompted, "Give the tree to your brother."

"No!" the owner of the garden flatly refused.

"What if you give the tree to your brother in exchange for a palm tree in Paradise?" offered the Prophet (s).

"No," persisted the man stubbornly.

The Prophet's companions looked on. Among them was Abu Ad-Dahdah (ra) *, who had been deep in thought as the exchange unfolded.

Suddenly, Abu Ad-Dahdah had an idea.

"Messenger of God," he proposed, "what if I bought the tree and gave it to the orphaned boy? Would I receive a palm tree in Paradise?"

"Yes," replied the Prophet (s).

Abu Ad-Dahdah then took stock of everything that he owned, wondering what he would need to tempt the stubborn man to give up his palm tree. He immediately thought of a piece of property he owned: on the land there were over six hundred palm trees, a well, and a home within the garden's boundaries. Abu Ad-Dahdah's garden was famous throughout Medina for its lush greenery and fertile land.

"Are you familiar with my garden?" Abu Ad-Dahdah asked the man.

"Of course!" said the man. "Who has not heard about

---

*   Acronym of "*radiyya Allahu anhu*" which translates to "may God be pleased with him." Common Islamic etiquette encourages such prayers to be made for the companions of the Prophet (pbuh) at the written or spoken mention of their names.

Abu Ad-Dahdah's wonderful garden?"

"Take my garden in exchange for the palm tree," said Abu Ad-Dahdah firmly.

The man stared at Abu Ad-Dahdah and then surveyed the faces of all those who were watching.

"Y-yes!" he sputtered finally. "I will accept your garden in exchange for the tree!"

Abu Ad-Dahdah turned to the orphan, "And now, I give you the palm tree. You may build your fence." The boy and his neighbor left, both content.

Abu Ad-Dahdah, however, was not yet satisfied.

"Prophet of God, is there a palm tree for me in Paradise now?" he asked.

"How many groves of trees there are!" exclaimed the Prophet. "How many trees there are, laden with fruit, awaiting you in Paradise!"

The satisfied Abu Ad-Dahdah headed toward his garden to collect some of his belongings. Outside the garden gates, he heard the joyous laughter of his wife and children relaxing under the shady trees. He now found himself hesitant to enter the beautiful garden. He did not want to see the dismay on their faces when he told them that the garden was no longer theirs.

Instead, he called out to his wife, "Um Ad-Dahdah!"

The wife replied, "Yes, Abu Ad-Dahdah!"

"Please come out of the garden," he called.

"Come out?" she questioned.

"Yes, I have sold it," Abu Ad-Dahdah told his wife.

"You sold our garden? To whom?" she asked, surprised.

"I sold the garden to my Lord, in exchange for a palm tree in Paradise," answered Abu Ad-Dahdah.

Um Ad-Dahdah cried, "God is great! What a wonderful bargain, Abu Ad-Dahdah!"

The mother gathered up her children and they took a final stroll around the beautiful property. At the garden gate, Um Ad-Dahdah checked the pockets of her children to make sure that all of the fruit and dates that they had been collecting throughout the day remained in the garden.

"These do not belong to us anymore," she whispered in her children's ears. "They belong to the Lord of the Worlds."

The blessed family walked out of the garden and happily closed the gates behind them. *

---

*   *Hadith* of the Prophet (s).

Lessons Learned:

1. **Protecting the rights of orphans.**

   When the orphaned youth in this story had a problem, he went to the Prophet Muhammad (s) for help. He knew that the Prophet assumed the responsibility of looking after orphans and helping them in their affairs. Unfortunately, other people often take advantage of children who have lost their parents. This was the reason why Prophet Muhammad (s) gave the young man's concern special attention. The Quran tells us, "So do not be harsh with the orphan." * We should not leave unprotected young people to fend for themselves. Instead, befriend them and advocate for them. The Prophet (s) advised, "Would you like for your heart to be softened and your goals to be met? Have mercy on the orphan, place your hand on his (or her) head, and feed him of your own food. This will soften your heart and fulfill your goals." **

2. **Use wisdom in solving disputes.**

   The Prophet (s) tried several ways to persuade the owner of the garden to give up the palm tree. First, he listened to the orphan's complaint and then verified what he had heard. He reasoned with the owner of the palm tree, asking him to give up his property for the sake of his brother. When that method was not effective, he offered a tree in Paradise for the exchange. The Prophet (s) could have simply ordered the man to give up his tree, but that would have been an injustice. Islam teaches that no one can be forced to buy or sell anything against his or her will. Instead, this problem would have to be solved using wisdom and creativity.

---

*   [Ad-Duha:9]
**   Narrated by Ahmed and At-Tabarani, sahih by Al-Albani.

3. Jump at the opportunity to do something good!

It is amazing how swiftly Abu Ad-Dahdah made his decision! He gave up his orchard of six-hundred trees for the sake of a reward he could neither see nor enjoy in this life. His wife, instead of being upset, praised her husband's decision to relinquish their most valuable possession. What could make them behave in this manner? It was their deep faith in God and their complete trust in the Prophet's (s) promise. Abu Ad-Dahdah truly believed in the verses of the Quran which describes the Prophet (s): "[The Prophet] does not speak from his own desire. It is nothing less than a revelation that is sent to him." * When the Prophet (s) promised a palm tree in Paradise, Abu Ad-Dahdah had no doubt that it was as real as anything in this world.

Abu Ad-Dahdah also understood the enormous importance Islam places on helping orphans and relieving their burdens. In fact, advocating for orphans is of high priority, as described in this verse: "Worship God: join nothing with Him. Be good to your parents, to relatives, to orphans, to the needy, to neighbors near and far, to travelers in need, and to your servants. God does not like arrogant, boastful people." ** Orphans are entitled to special consideration in Islam.

Finally, Abu Ad-Dahdah knew that charity does not decrease one's wealth in the slightest. Provisions, blessings, and income rest in the hands of God alone. This world will vanish one day, and only the Hereafter will remain. Charity is an investment for the afterlife to come.

---

* [an-Najm:3-4]
** [an-Nisa:36]

4. **A supportive marriage is the key to success.**

When Abu Ad-Dahdah asked his family to leave the garden, his wife did not complain. She demanded no explanation, but instead whole-heartedly approved of her husband's act of charity. Because of her unconditional support, she shared equally in Abu Ad-Dahdah's reward. Perhaps Abu Ad-Dahdah's confidence in his wife's support helped him arrive at his decision. He knew that she would readily give up anything for the sake of God. The Quran says, "None of you will attain true piety unless you give out of what you cherish: whatever you give, God knows about it very well." * Mutual support and understanding are the sustainers of a marriage.

5. **Believers fulfill their promises and trusts.**

Um Ad-Dahdah was so scrupulous and trustworthy that she did not remove any fruit from the garden once the garden no longer belonged to her family. She did not even allow her children to eat dates that were already in their pockets. The word of the believer is a guarantee. God says in the Quran, "Stay well away from the property of orphans, except with the best of intentions, until they come of age; give full measure and weight, according to justice. We do not burden any soul with more than it can bear. When you speak, be just, even if it concerns a relative; keep any promises you make in God's name. This is what He commands you to do, so that you may take heed." **

---

*   [Aal-Imran:92]
**   [Al-Anam:152]

"Believers, avoid making too many suspicions — some assumptions are sinful — and do not spy on one another or speak ill of people behind their backs: would any of you like to eat the flesh of your dead brother? No, you would hate it. So be mindful of God; God is ever Relenting, most Merciful."

[Al-Hujurat:12]

— 3 —
A Plate of Dates
The Sin of Backbiting

One evening, there was a persistent knock at the door of Al-Hasan Al-Basri, an early Muslim scholar who was famous for his knowledge and piety. Al-Hasan opened the door and asked the visitor what he needed.

"Oh, Abu Saʿeed," exclaimed the man, addressing Al-Hasan by his nickname. "If you had attended the gathering of so-and-so this afternoon, you would have heard him speak poorly of you!"

Al-Hasan's face instantly changed.

"I seek refuge in God! Are you the only one Satan could find to send my way?" Then Al-Hasan asked the man to leave and shut the door promptly.

Soon after, Al-Hasan arranged some fresh dates on a plate, wrapped them neatly, and carried them to a nearby house. But this was not just any neighbor's home — in it lived the man who had gossiped about him earlier that day.

When the door opened, Al-Hasan presented the dates and said, "I heard that earlier today you gave me the gift of some of your good deeds. So I wished to present you with something in exchange. Please take this gift, and may God reward you in goodness." *

*   Rawa'i al-Urayfi pg. 96.

Lessons Learned:

1. Spreading gossip is wrong.

The man who knocked on Al-Hasan's door committed a sin: He passed along gossip he had heard earlier at a gathering. Informing a person about words spoken about him is almost as bad as the gossip itself. Prophet Muhammad (s) said in his last Hajj sermon, "Your blood, your property, and your reputations are not to be violated, as sacred to one another as this day of Hajj, in this holy month, in this holy land. Have I not conveyed the message?" * What goes on in a social setting is privileged information, and it should not be conveyed to those who were not present. When a person transfers gossip, he or she is actually contributing to this evil by spreading it further and by fostering bad feelings between people.

2. Backbiting infuriates the hearts.

Al-Hasan understood how backbiting enrages the hearts, and that is why he disapprovingly sent the visitor away from his door. The man who carried the gossip to Al-Hasan's tried to incite the scholar to become entangled in resentment and anger. Instead, Al-Hasan sent him away. The Prophet (s) said, "Do you know what gheeba (backbiting) is?" The companions replied that only God and the Prophet (s) would know. The Prophet (s) explained, "It is mentioning your brother in a way that would upset him." The companions asked, "What if we described something that was true?" The Prophet (s) said, "If what you say is true, then it is backbiting. If what you say is not true, then it is slander." ** Developing the habit of never conveying any negative talk will make much of the fighting and resentment between people disappear.

---

*   Agreed upon.
**   Narrated by Muslim.

3. **Respond to poor behavior with excellence.**

Al-Hasan Al-Basri did not allow Satan to get away with his tricks. First, he sent the bearer of gossip away, refusing to participate in the turmoil. He then examined his own intentions and purified his heart. Lastly, he prepared a sincere gift for the person who had spoken ill of him. Al-Hasan followed the Quran's advice: "Good and evil cannot be equal. Repel evil with what is better and your enemy will become as close as an old and valued friend." * Try to become someone who translates the words of the Quran into action. Act kindly even when feeling mistreated to repel Satan from the heart.

4. **Correct mistakes in a beautiful manner.**

Al-Hasan understood that even the best of people make mistakes sometimes. It was not enough for Al-Hasan to purify what was in his own heart; he took it upon himself to gently correct his brother, showing him the right way. Al-Hasan alerted the gossiper that carelessness with his tongue had cost him some of his good deeds. Through his gift, Al-Hasan gently sent the message: "Be careful, my brother! Do not lose your good deeds because you cannot control your tongue!" Gift giving also naturally draws hearts closer together.

5. **Backbiting embarrasses the speaker.**

Even though it was Al-Hasan who was insulted and defamed at the gathering, it was the backbiter who was humiliated at the end. Gossip eventually shames everyone who is involved, the speaker and the listeners. It is best to protect oneself from backbiting altogether, avoiding the risk of ruining reputations, good deeds, and self-respect among friends.

---

*   [Al-Fussilat:34]

The wise man Luqman advised his son, "My son, heed these words from me and you will live in honor. Extend your noble character to both friend and stranger. Withhold your ignorance from the noble among people and the ignoble. Guard your brothers and care for your relatives. Save them the indignity of ill-intentioned people who would speak badly of them. Choose brothers whom, when you part ways, will speak no ill of you nor you of them."

Al-Mawsu'ah Ash-Shamilah
(v.1, p. 46)

— 4 —

Forgive and Forget

Rejecting Rumors

Once a man entered the presence of Caliph Umar ibn Abdul Aziz. He then told an incriminating tale about another person.

The Caliph said, "If you would like, we can investigate the story you have brought to me. However, please beware; if you have lied about this story, you will be among the people described in the verse: 'Believers, if a troublemaker brings you news, check it first, in case you wrong others unwittingly and later regret what you have done.' * And if you have told the truth, you will be among those described in another verse: 'Backbiter, slander-monger...' **

---

*   [Al-Hujurat:6]
**   [Al-Qalam:11]

"Or," the Caliph continued, "we can forget and forgive what you have said."

The Caliph's visitor cried out, "Forgive me, Leader of the Believers! I will not speak of this again!" [*]

*   From the book Dalil As-Sa'ileen by Anas Ismail Abu Dawud, pg. 618-619.

Lessons Learned:

1. Defamation is destructive.

Umar recognized that people who tell tales to those in charge, such as teachers, parents, or employers, are usually motivated by jealousy or resentment. Telling tales ruins relationships and promotes a cycle of enmity. It is met with punishment in this life and in the next, as described in the Quran: "A painful torment awaits in this world and the next for those who like indecency to spread among the believers; God knows and you do not." * That is why Umar decisively stopped the gossip in its tracks. When people begin to speak negatively about others, do not remain in their company. Participating in their talk only encourages bad feelings, betrayal, and resentment.

2. Foresight and intelligent reasoning can right a wrong.

The Caliph did not become caught up in the tale his visitor was telling. Instead, he used good character, logical reasoning, and swift intelligence to present a proposal which diffused the situation. The Caliph possessed knowledge of the Quran and strong communication skills. He allowed his visitor to recognize his own mistake and repent. There is much to learn from the Caliph's example. He skillfully and politely took the opportunity to bring the gossip to a halt. The consequence for gossipping is great, so this behavior should be corrected immediately. The Quran says, "Woe to every fault-finding backbiter!" **

3. Verify rumors first.

Caliph Umar taught us how to stop a rumor: to treat it as a lie until it can be confirmed. The Prophet (s) said, "One would be enough of a liar if he was to talk about

---

*   [An-Noor:19]
**   [Al-Humaza:1]

25

everything he heard." * Be careful not to circulate hearsay without confirming that it is true. Otherwise it might be recorded as a lie in one's Book of Deeds.

4. **Gentleness and love are the foundations of justice.**

Instead of using his authority to intimidate his visitor, the Caliph used gentle reasoning to empowered the man to choose a better way. A great level of understanding and strong character is required to inspire others to acknowledge their mistakes and to repent on their own volition. It may be easier to use intimidation and force to get quick results; however, this will always be less effective in changing hearts. Adults or children who are corrected in a gentle manner as displayed by Caliph Umar will internalize the lesson deeply, making it less likely to fall back into the same mistake.

"'What drove you to the scorching fire?' They will answer, 'We did not pray; we did not feed the poor; we indulged with others; we denied the Day of Judgment, until the Certain End came upon us.'"

[Al-Mudathir:42-47]

— 5 —
The Beggar and the Chicken
Compassion for the Needy

Once a man and his wife were enjoying a meal together. On the table before them was a warm, juicy roasted chicken. As they began their delicious meal, there was a knock at the door. The man of the house got up to find it was a beggar. Annoyed by the disruption, he drove the poor soul off of his doorstep empty-handed.

Several years passed, and by this time the man had lost his job, become extremely needy, and divorced his wife. Not long after, the wife remarried.

One day, the woman and her new husband sat down to eat a juicy, roasted chicken, similar to the one she had prepared many years prior in a different home.

A beggar knocked at the door.

The new husband told his wife, "Wrap up the chicken neatly and offer it to the man outside," his voice brimming with sympathy and grace.

The wife wrapped up the chicken and took it to the door. To her shock, she recognized the beggar. She handed him the food and quickly shut the door.

When the new husband found his wife weeping, he asked her what was the matter.

"The beggar was my former husband!" she explained. "I was reminded that many years ago, a beggar came to our door and my ex-husband sent the poor man away instead of giving him some of our food."

The new husband smiled and said, "Would you like to hear something even stranger still?" he asked. "The first beggar who came to your home many years ago … was me." *

*   Anees As-Saliheen wa Sameer Al-Muttaqeen, by Muhammad AlJundi, p. 219.

Lessons Learned:

1. **The seeker should not be turned away.**

   It is not always the beggar who asks. People may be turned away in their search for answers or quest for knowledge. We should never deem a question as too trivial or make others feel embarrassed about their ignorance. God says in the Quran, "God took a pledge from those who were given the Scripture — 'Make it known to people; do not conceal it.'" * This also applies to needy people who ask for money, food, or favors. If one cannot give, or does not feel there is a true need, then the request could be declined politely and kindly. Never meet a request with rudeness or harshness. Instead, follow the command of the Quran: "And do not chide the one who asks for help." **

2. **As one gives, one will receive.**

   The first husband turned away the beggar, never imagining that one day he would be in the poor man's shoes. Be careful never to hurt someone with words or poor manners. Do not ignore or belittle people and only use good character when dealing with others. Someday, any one of us could become vulnerable and in need. Perhaps we will be treated as we used to treat others. God says, "Your Lord is always on the watch." ***

3. **Mistreating others leads to loss of blessings.**

   The selfish man made the beggar feel ashamed of asking for help. He turned away the beggar for having dared to knock at his door. Not long after, this same man began to lose one blessing after another: his livelihood, his home, and his wife. God tells us in the Quran that people may

---

*	[Aal-Imran:187]
**	[Ad-Duha:10]
***	[Al-Fajr:14]

meet the consequences of their injustice during their lifetime: "Corruption has flourished on land and sea as a result of people's actions, and He will make them taste the consequences of some of their own actions so that they may turn back." [*]

4. Bad experiences may be a catalyst for good.

The beggar had a door slammed in his face in a humiliating rejection. But perhaps this experience motivated him to change his situation and pursue a better life. Somehow, this beggar eventually found a job, a home, and a wife. More than that, he was determined to treat any beggar who came to his door with respect and kindness. In fact, when the hungry beggar knocked, he did not offer him a small donation or a morsel of food. He gave the beggar the entire chicken that he was planning to enjoy himself. He treated the beggar with the respect of an honored guest. Therefore, this former beggar's life became a source of goodness and comfort to others, all because someone had once slammed the door in his face. God says in the Quran, "You may dislike something although it is good for you, or you may like something although it is bad for you." [**] Sometimes, one benefits most from life's adversities.

[*]   [Ar-Rum:41]
[**]   [Al-Baqarah:216]

The Prophet (s) said

---

*"Whoever bears arms against us
is not one of us,
and whoever cheats us
is not one of us."*

Narrated by Muslim

— 6 —

The Man Who Tricked His Donkey

Honesty in Every Situation

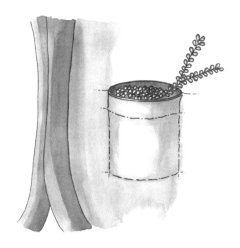

Imam Ahmad ibn Hanbal was a great collector and compiler of *ahadith*, or sayings, of the Prophet (s). He once heard that there was a *hadith* to be collected in the distant city of Damascus. For this reason, Imam Ahmad travelled 800 kilometers from Baghdad to Damascus just to meet the person who would narrate the hadith to him.

It was the custom of hadith compilers like Imam Ahmed to conduct thorough investigations into the narrator's character, history, and the chain of narration tracing back to Prophet Muhammad (s). If there was even the slightest doubt about the character or memory of the narrator, Imam Ahmad would reject the hadith, no matter how far he had journeyed to record it.

When Imam Ahmad arrived in Damascus, he began to inquire about the man who would narrate the hadith. He asked about his character, the accuracy of his memory, his habits, and his dealings with other people. After meticulous examination, Imam Ahmad put on his best clothes, applied cologne, and went to the man's house early in the morning. He found the learned man in front of his house, preparing his donkey for the day's work. The donkey seemed uncooperative. Imam Ahmad paused at a distance to watch the scene unfold.

The donkey dug in its heels and the man tugged at the reins, but it was no use. The donkey would not budge. Frustrated, the man gently held out the folds of his robes and shook them, as if grain were inside. The donkey, motivated by the suggestion of food, trotted forward.

Imam Ahmad wondered if the man truly held grain in his robe. When he moved closer, he saw that the man's robe was empty.

Imam Ahmad turned away from the scholar and his donkey and began the 800-kilometer journey back to Baghdad. He returned home without ever speaking to the man, or fulfilling the mission for which he had travelled so far. According to Imam Ahmad's stringent standards, if a man was willing to deceive a simple animal, he could not be trusted to convey the words of Prophet Muhammad (s) to the many generations of Muslims to follow him. [*]

_____

[*]   From Dalil As-Sa'ileen by Anas Ismail Abu Dawud, p. 541.

Lessons Learned:

1. **Learning is an obligation.**

   Imam Ahmad embraced the pursuit of knowledge with all of his being. He studied and taught others, made good use of every second of his time, and went to great lengths to seek knowledge. In this story, Imam Ahmad embarked upon a long journey to obtain a single saying of the Prophet (s), hoping for a reward from God for every step along his path. The Prophet (s) said, "Whoever pursues a path to knowledge, God will ease a path to Paradise for him." * We can learn from this story that it is not enough for us to consume information from lectures, social media, or computer screens. Instead, we should also actively seek out learning at a deeper level by reading books from reliable sources. Once we have verified the authenticity of what we have learned, we can then share it with others.

2. **Character outweighs knowledge.**

   When we absorb knowledge from scholars or teachers, we should make sure that their speech and behavior is aligned with the beautiful words that they preach. God says in the Quran, "But those of them who are well grounded in knowledge and have faith do believe in what has been revealed to you and in what was revealed before you - those who perform the prayers, pay the prescribed alms, and believe in God and the Last Day - to them We shall give a great reward." **

3. **Respect the Prophet (s).**

   Imam Ahmad washed, dressed, and perfumed himself before setting out to investigate the sayings of the Prophet

---

*   Narrated by Muslim.
**   [Al-Nisa:162]

(s). Imam Ahmad had such habits whenever he intended to speak or write about the Prophet (s), or learn new information about him. Showing such a degree of respect for learning about the Prophet (s), one can only imagine how carefully Imam Ahmad may have implemented the Prophet's example. Believers show respect for the Prophet (s) by applying his example to our own actions.

4. **Dishonesty negates trust.**

By deceiving the donkey, the scholar showed a lack of respect for honesty. An honest person is unconditionally truthful to all beings, including children and animals. Imam Ahmad could not trust the man once he had witnessed his deceitful, albeit minor, offense. God says, "Falsehood is fabricated only by those who do not believe in God's revelation: they are the liars." * One might defend the scholar, arguing that even though he had tricked an animal, it did not necessarily imply that he would lie about religious knowledge. However, lying is a habit that often begins with small offenses. Like any other illness, it spreads until it leads a person to the habit of dishonesty.

"God has forbidden undutifulness to your mothers, burying your daughters alive, and withholding what should be given. He dislikes excessive talk about other people, asking too many questions, and wasting money."

Agreed upon

— 7 —

Juha's Donkey

Worrying about People's Opinions

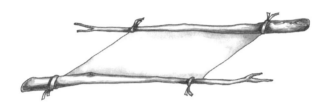

Juha, a legendary character known for his tall-tale adventures, was worried about his son. The young boy cared too much about the opinions of other people. Before he would listen to his father, he always wondered, "What will my friends think?"

Juha decided to teach his son a lesson, so he brought the boy along on one of his errands. Juha rode on the back of their donkey, while his son walked at his side.

Before long, a group of women walked by the two companions.

The meddlesome women glared at Juha and scolded, "Look at that cruel father! He rides the donkey himself, while the poor boy is walking on foot!"

Juha halted the donkey, climbed down, and lifted his son on to the animal's back. They then continued on their way.

Soon they passed by some old men who were resting in a sunny field. One of the men noticed Juha and his boy, and sneered as he pointed them out to his friends. They all shook their heads disapprovingly.

"Poor man!" one said. "He is spoiling his son, allowing him to ride while he himself is walking! How does he expect the boy to learn good manners and respect for his elders?"

Juha turned to his son and said, "Did you hear what they said? Let's both ride the donkey."

So the father and son continued on their journey, both on the donkey's back.

Soon they came across another group of people who cried out, "Fear God! Together you are much too heavy for the donkey. How can you burden that poor animal so?"

So Juha dismounted from the donkey and helped his son climb down.

The boy said, "Did you hear what those people said? Let's walk and let the donkey rest so that people don't speak so badly of us."

The donkey plodded along, followed by a weary Juha and his son. Soon, a group of people saw the two exhausted travelers and began to laugh and jeer.

"Look at those crazy people! They look so tired, but they have a donkey walking right in front of them! Maybe they should carry the donkey and pamper him even more!"

Juha and his son looked at each other. They walked over to a tree by the side of the road, broke off a large branch, and created a makeshift stretcher. Each of them held one end of the stretcher, and they began to carry the donkey down the road.

A throng of people began to follow them, laughing at the spectacle of Juha and his son carrying their donkey on a stretcher. An officer soon arrived and chased the onlookers away, presuming that the man and his son were clearly insane.

Having illustrated his point, Juha then turned to his son with some advice: "My boy, this is what happens to anyone who tries too hard to please others. Don't care so much about what people have to say!" *

*   Anees As-Saliheen wa Sameer Al-Muttaqeen, by Muhammad AlJundi.

Lessons Learned:

1. First-hand experience is the best teacher.

Lecturing is not always the best way to teach a lesson. Providing the opportunity for hands-on experience is often the best way to get important ideas across. In fact, sometimes the only way for children to learn is by trying something out for themselves and making their own mistakes.

2. It is impossible to please everyone.

If we try to make everyone happy, one group might be satisfied while another will complain. Imam Al-Shafi'i advised one of his friends about this problem: "Abu Musa, it is impossible to please everyone. you will never be exempt from criticism. So seek out what is beneficial to you, and let people think what they will." Believers should focus on what pleases God without worrying about what other people might think. Do not allow the judgement of others to interfere with one's ideas or to be a diversion from one's own lofty plans.

3. Be kind to animals.

In his haste to teach his son a lesson, Juha failed to realize that he was overburdening his donkey. Even if we are preoccupied or in a hurry, we should not neglect the people, the animals, or the environment around us. The believer must take care of all that inhabit the earth, as Prophet Muhammad (s) said: "Have mercy toward those on the earth so that the One in the sky has mercy upon you." *

4. There are ways to handle bad advice.

Some of the people whom Juha encountered had

---

*   Narrated by Al-Albani.

reasonable concerns from their own perspectives. The final group, however, only wished to see Juha disgraced. Their bad suggestion of carrying the donkey was only meant to humiliate Juha and his son. When people of bad character lend advice, it is best to disregard it.

God says

"The Messenger believes in what has been sent down to him from his Lord, as do the faithful. They all believe in God, His angels, His scriptures, and His messengers. They say, 'We make no distinction between one another of His messengers,' and they say, 'We hear and we obey. Grant us forgiveness, our Lord; to You we all return.'"

[Al-Baqarah:285]

— 8 —

The Prophet's Dream
Punishments in the Grave

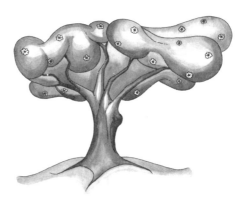

Samurah ibn Jundub, one of the Companions of the Prophet (s), related this *hadith*:

After the Prophet (s) would complete his prayer, he would turn to us and ask, "Who among you had a dream last night?" Anyone who had a dream would share it with the others, and the Prophet (s) would respond, "*Masha'Allah*." *

One day, when the Prophet (s) asked if anyone had seen a dream, none of us responded. So the Prophet (s) began to speak, telling us about his own dream:

"I had a dream last night," he said. "Two men came to me, took my hand, and led me to the Holy Land. There I

---

*   "It is as God wills!"

saw a man with an iron hook standing over another man. He placed the hook into the corner of the man's mouth and tore off the side of his face. Then he repeated this action on the other side. As soon as he completed tearing off one side of the face, the other would return to its normal state, and the process would begin again.

"I asked, 'What is happening?' But the two men only told me to proceed.

"We came upon a man lying flat on his back. Another man stood over his head, holding a large rock. He threw the rock on the man's head as he lay on the ground. As soon as the standing man had retrieved the rock, the head of the man on the ground returned to its original state.

"I asked my companions about this, but they told me to move on.

"So we continued until we came across something like a Tannoor, a clay-lined pit in the ground, used to bake bread. The opening of the oven was small, but the inside was huge. A fire was burning in its depths, and it was filled with naked men and women. When the fire blazed forth, the men and women would scramble up the sides of the oven, almost to the top, but when the flames receded they would climb back down.

"I asked my companions, 'What is happening?' But they only said, 'Proceed!'

"We then came to a river of blood. On its banks stood one man, while another was swimming in the river. Whenever the man in the river tried to swim to shore, the man standing on the bank would throw stones into his mouth.

"'What is happening?' I asked. My companions did not respond, but ordered me to continue.

"We finally came to a lush, green garden. A majestic tree stood in the garden, and under its shade sat an old man surrounded by children. Near the tree was another man lighting a fire. We climbed the tree and reached a magnificent house, the likes of which I had never seen, filled with people of all ages. We continued to ascend upward, and I found myself in a mansion even larger than the one before.

"I turned to my companions and said, 'I have come across many wonders tonight. Tell me about what I have seen.'

"'Yes,' they said. 'We shall tell you. The man whose mouth was torn by the hook was a liar who told lies until they spread around the entire world. He will endure the punishment of the hook until the Day of Judgment.

"'The one whose head was crushed by the rock was someone whom God had taught the Quran. He used to spend his nights sleeping, rather than reciting the Quran, and he did not apply its teachings during the day. He will endure this punishment until the Day of Judgment. The people whom you saw in the pit were adulterers. The man in the river used to collect interest.

"'As for the old man under the tree, that was Prophet Abraham (as). The children surrounding him were those who passed away while they were still very young. The man lighting the fire was Malik, the guardian of Hell. The first house you entered was the house of the believers, and the higher, more spacious dwelling was the home of the martyrs.

"'I am the Angel Gabriel, and this is the Angel Michael. Now look up!'

"I looked up and saw an abode in the clouds.

"The two angels said, 'That is your home.'

"'Let me enter it!' I said.

"They replied, 'You still have time left on Earth. When you complete that time, you will be able to enter your home.'" *

*   Narrated by Bukhari and Muslim.

Lessons Learned:

1. How the Prophet (s) captured attention.

The Prophet (s), in his conversations, teachings, and actions, caught the attention of his audience, using various approaches to engage his listeners. He applied teaching methods which captivated the eyes, ears, and imaginations of his followers to help them understand particular principles. When the Prophet (s) asked, "Who had a dream last night?" he opened up a discussion which aroused the interest of the Companions. We can learn through this example that almost any subject may be introduced in an intriguing way. We can deliver important messages, especially about faith, in a captivating, interesting manner.

2. The punishment for lying.

Lying is one of the most dangerous sins, with severe consequences in this life and in the Afterlife. It prevents people from trusting and respecting one another. The more a lie spreads, the more damaging it becomes. False rumors and fabricated news can destroy people's lives. The Prophet (s) said, "Lying leads to shamelessness, and shamelessness leads to Hellfire. A man will keep telling lies until one day it will be written that he is a liar." * The punishment in the grave for lying is a dreadful one, as described in the dream of the Prophet (s). A hook will tear the liar's face from the corner of the mouth to the back of the neck, over and over again until the Day of Judgment. This will not be a physical punishment after death, but rather a spiritual punishment in the grave, much like someone who dreams of something terrible, feeling pain and fear, but cannot wake up. When the Day of Judgment arrives, liars will meet their real punishment,

---

*   Narrated by Bukhari and Muslim.

the physical torment of Hellfire. May God protect all of his servants from this punishment.

3. The Quran should make an impact on the reciter.

God honored humans by giving them a powerful and wonderful message from Him. He taught us how to read, understand, and apply its teachings. When we recite the Quran during the day or night, heeding its commands and advice, we thank God. Those who know the Quran well but do not act upon its teachings will be punished. "Will they not contemplate the Quran? Do they have locks on their hearts? Those who turn on their heels after being shown guidance are duped and tempted by Satan." [*] The vivid punishment described in the dream, where a heavy rock is hurled at a man's head repeatedly, is the fate of someone who ignores the guidance of the Quran even after reciting and understanding it.

4. The punishment of adultery.

When God created the world, He instituted the system of marriage in order to protect progeny, safeguard lineage, satisfy human desire, and preserve the morality and nobility of human beings. Those who choose to indulge in desires outside of marriage forfeit the morality and nobility given to them by God. He warns us to stay far away from adultery, or anything that may lead to it: "And do not go anywhere near adultery: it is an outrage and an evil path." [**] The punishment for adultery is humiliation, poverty, and misguidance in this life, as well as misery in the Hereafter.

[*]   [Muhammad:24-25]
[**]   [Issra:32]

5. **The punishment of consuming interest.**

Within the laws dictated by God are rules to ensure that people's earnings are not wasted. Usury, or collecting interest, is forbidden because it harms some individuals in society. Interest is when someone loans money with the condition that it should be returned in full with an extra fee - the later the loan is returned the more the debtor must pay. Interest prevents beneficial favors among people. It makes the rich richer and the poor poorer, makes the repayment of debt more difficult, and capitalizes on people's misfortune. God says in the Quran, "You who believe, do not consume usurious interest, doubled and redoubled." * The person who collects interest is considered a thief and a predator, taking advantage of people's vulnerability. After death, the collector of the interest will swim in a river of blood, just as he swam in the savings of those around him.

6. **The objectives of shariah.**

The laws which God revealed, the shariah, are designed to preserve life and uplift humanity. The main objectives of the shariah are to preserve faith, intellect, property, family, and human life. When anything is forbidden in Islam, it is because it undermines one of these objectives. For example, adultery violates the objective of protecting the sanctity of family. When adultery is rampant, it is difficult for families to stay intact and for children to know their parents. Collecting interest violates the objective of preserving people's property. Our intellect is protected when knowledge, especially Quranic knowledge, is learned for the benefit of oneself and the community.

---

*   [Aal Imran:130]

Belief in the angels.

Angels are special beings created from light. They inhabit the sky, are assigned various responsibilities, and can take on different forms. The story shows us how angels led the Prophet (s) to understand different dimensions. Among the angels are Gabriel, the angel responsible for revelation, Malik, the guardian of Hellfire, and Michael, the distributor of provisions and rain. Angels are free of mistakes or sin, and God says in the Quran, "Believers, guard yourselves and your families against a Fire whose fuel is people and stones, over which stand angels, stern and strong; angels who never disobey God's commands to them, but do as they are ordered." ˙ Muslims believe in the angels and take inspiration from their diligent worship. The Quran says, "The Messenger believes in what has been sent down to him from his Lord, as do the faithful. They all believe in God, His angels, His scriptures, and His messengers. 'We make no distinction between any of His messengers,' they say, 'We hear and obey. Grant us Your forgiveness, our Lord. To You we all return!'" ˙˙

[At-Tahreem:6]
[Al-Baqarah:285]

God says

"Remember when Moses said to his people, 'God commands you to sacrifice a cow.' They said, 'Are you making fun of us?' He answered, 'God forbid that I should be so ignorant.' They said, 'Call on your Lord for us, to show us what sort of cow it should be.' He answered, 'God says it should be neither too old nor too young, but in between, so do as you are commanded.' They said, 'Call on your Lord for us, to show us what color it should be.' He answered, 'God says it should be a bright yellow cow, pleasing to the eye.' They said, 'Call on your Lord for us, to show us exactly what it is: all cows are more or less alike to us. With God's will, we shall be guided.' He replied, 'It is a perfect and unblemished cow, not trained to till the earth or water the fields.' They said, 'Now you have brought the truth,' and so they slaughtered it, though they almost failed to do so. Then, when you killed someone and started to blame one another – although God was to bring what you had concealed to light– We said, 'Strike the [body] with a part of [the cow]': thus God brings the dead to life and shows His signs so that you may understand. Even after that, your hearts became as hard as rocks, or even harder, for there are rocks from which streams spring out, and some from which water comes when they split open, and others which fall down in awe of God: He is not unaware of what you do."

[Al-Baqarah:67-74]

52

— 9 —

Too Many Questions

A Lesson from Surah Al-Baqarah

A murder was committed among the Israelites, also known as *Banu Israel*. The victim was a wealthy man, but his tribesmen could not identify the killer. Instead, they began to blame one another for the crime. Finally, they decided to take the matter to Prophet Moses (as). They brought the dead man's body before Moses and asked him to help them find the killer.

Upon hearing the story, Prophet Moses (as) replied, "I do not know the answer."

"Then ask your Lord to reveal it to you!" they pleaded. So Moses asked his Lord, but the answer did not come right away.

Instead, God told Moses to command Banu Israel to sacrifice a cow.

"Are you joking?" said the Israelites in disbelief.

"I seek refuge in God from being among the ignorant," responded Moses.

Banu Israel hesitated to obey the command right away. Instead, they asked him for the age of the cow. Moses responded that the cow should be neither too young nor too old.

"What color should it be?" Banu Israel asked further.

Moses described a cow with a bright yellow coat, brilliant and pleasing to the eye.

The Israelites asked for more specific details, stalling and complaining that cows look very similar to one another. So Prophet Moses described a cow that was not used for work, nor for plowing the earth or watering the fields. In fact, it should be a cow without a single flaw or blemish.

The Israelites searched the land for such an exceptional cow. Finally, they found one that matched the description Moses (as) had given. Because this was such a rare cow, they were obliged to purchase it for an exceptionally high price.

They slaughtered the cow and took it to Prophet Moses (as). Prophet Moses (as) took a bone from the cow and struck the body of the murdered man. Before their very eyes, the dead man came to life. He identified the killer and then died once more, to everyone's wonder.

Although the mystery was solved, Banu Israel had shown their reluctance in slaughtering the cow, asking question after question about the details of the animal to be sacrificed. When the Israelites witnessed the dead come to life before their eyes, it did not cause their hearts to soften and draw closer to God. Instead, the hearts of Banu Israel became colder and more resistant, until they became as hard as stone. [*]

[*] Al-Qissah Al-Quraniyyah Hidayah wa Bayan, by Dr. Wahbah Al-Zuhayli, 1992.

Lessons Learned:

1. **Too much questioning makes religion difficult.**

   Through this story, God teaches us not to ask too many questions in matters that may only become more difficult when we discover the answer. Banu Israel were commanded to sacrifice a cow: it could have been any ordinary cow if they had hastened to obey. Instead, they continued to ask questions, making it difficult to find a cow that met all of the requirements. Prophet Muhammad (s) said, "What I have forbidden for you, avoid. What I have ordered you, do as much of it as you can. For verily, it was only their excessive questioning and disagreeing with their Prophets that destroyed the nations who came before you." *

2. **Belief in the Last Day.**

   A human being is alive only because of the will and power of God. In sacrificing the cow, Banu Israel were reminded that God is the One who brings life to the dead and death to the living. Striking a dead body with a cow's bone could only bring the dead to life if God willed this. Otherwise, it would be impossible. The Quran says, "This is because God is the truth; He brings the dead back to life; He has power over everything. There is no doubt that the Last Hour is bound to come, nor that God will raise the dead from their graves." ** All of us will die and be judged, so we should prepare ourselves to stand before God by accruing good deeds and by succeeding in the tests of this earthly life.

---

*   Narrated by Bukhari and Muslim.

**   [Al-Hajj:6-7]

3. **Practical application is better than theory.**

God was capable of bringing the dead man to life without striking the corpse with a cow's bone. However, he taught Banu Israel the importance of making an effort. The answer to their question would come to them only after they had slaughtered the cow, brought it to Prophet Moses (as), and struck the dead body with a piece of another dead being. Hands-on experience and visual presentation often convey stronger meanings than just words.

4. **Arrogance hardens and blinds the hearts.**

Even though God brought the dead to life before their eyes, the Israelites continued to be weak in faith, insistent in their wrongdoing, and insensitive to guidance. Even when someone witnesses a miracle with his own eyes, his heart may be too hard to accept guidance. God says in the Quran, "Have these people not travelled through the land with hearts to understand and ears to hear? It is not people's eyes that are blind, but their hearts within their chests." * When confronted with the truth, such people respond only with silence, stillness, and hesitation.

"No misfortune can happen, either in the earth or in yourselves, that was not set down in writing before We brought it into being — that is easy for God. So you need not grieve for what you miss nor gloat over what you gain. God does not love the conceited, the boastful."

[Al-Hadid:22-23]

— 10 —

The Patience of Urwa

Turning to God in Tragedy

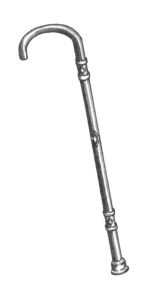

Caliph Al-Waleed ibn Abd Al-Malik had long awaited a visit from his cousin, Urwa ibn Az-Zubayr. The distance between Urwa's home in Medina to the capital, Damascus, was a daunting journey of a thousand kilometers. At last, Urwa set out on the long journey to visit his cousin, the caliph. He brought his young son along with him on the trip.

During the difficult journey, Urwa fell ill. A wound in his leg became dangerously infected. The problem worsened until he could no longer walk. When Urwa finally arrived in Damascus, he had to be carried into the city.

The caliph was alarmed when he observed Urwa's condition, and he was saddened that his visitors had experienced hardship on their journey. The caliph summoned the finest doctors in Damascus to treat his cousin. They examined Urwa's infected leg, and they determined that the only option was amputation.

The physicians began to prepare Urwa for the difficult operation. As was the standard for such a procedure, the doctors offered Urwa some wine to dull the pain.

Urwa refused. "How can I drink something my Lord has forbidden in His Book?" he questioned. The doctors were at a loss. They felt the operation would be impossible without something to ease Urwa's pain.

"What other alternative is there?" the physicians asked their patient.

"Let me pray," Urwa replied. "Once I have settled in my prostration, you may proceed with the operation."

And so Urwa prayed. The physicians waited until Urwa was on his knees in *sujood.* * While he was prostrate, the doctors amputated his leg. During the entire procedure, Urwa was still and calm, lost in concentration, engaged in the worship of God. His devotion was the ultimate anesthetic.

Finally, in order to stop the bleeding, the physicians poured hot oil onto the amputation site. Only then did Urwa lose consciousness.

Meanwhile, a tragedy had occurred outside the palace walls. Urwa's young son, who had travelled with him from Medina, had been observing the horses in the caliph's stables. One of the horses had kicked the boy, and the blow had killed the child instantly.

---

* The prostration in prayer.

The caliph was devastated at the news, first of the loss of Urwa's leg, and then about the boy's death. Caliph Al-Waleed ibn Abd Al-Malik could not find words to speak to his cousin. Finally, he sat by Urwa's bedside and spoke to him gently: "May God grant you solace in your illness." The Caliph continued, "And may God grant you solace in your son's death."

Urwa replied in a voice brimming with patience and faith, "To God is all praise, to Him we belong, and to Him we shall return. My Lord gave me seven sons and took one of them. He gave me four limbs and took one of them. When He afflicts, he also relieves, and when He takes, He also gives. I ask God to reunite me with both my son and my lost limb in Heaven."

Over the coming weeks, Urwa gradually recovered. He was soon able to make his way about the city with the help of a cane. One day, he entered into the caliph's court to find an old man with a scarred face and sightless eyes.

The caliph beckoned to Urwa and said, "Ask this man to tell you about his life."

So Urwa asked, "Shaikh, what is your story?"

The old man turned to Urwa and told his tale: "I once lived in a valley where there was no one who had more wealth, children, or good fortune than I. But one fateful night, a terrible flood came. The water took my riches, most of my family, and everything that I possessed. When the sun rose the next day, I was left with nothing but a donkey and one infant child. Suddenly, the donkey bolted away. I ran after it, but then I heard my little child crying. I hurried back as fast as I could, but I found that a wolf had pounced upon my son! I was too late to save him. There was nothing that I could do. I then ran back to the donkey, but the beast kicked me so hard that he left me blind, with my face horribly scarred."

Urwa asked, "How did you react to these tragedies?"

The old man replied resolutely, "I say: all praise to God who left me with a strong heart and a tongue that remembers Him." *

*   From the book Ahsan Al-Mahasin by Abu Ishaq al-Ruqiy, p. 166.

Lessons Learned:

1. The importance of visiting relatives.

Urwa travelled to visit his cousin in a far-away city. As with any good action, the finer and more numerous the intentions, the greater the reward. Urwa carried many good intentions in his heart: fostering love for the sake of God; strengthening of bonds among relatives; responding to the invitation from a caliph; and following the example of Prophet Muhammad (s).

The Prophet (s) said, "A man once set out to visit a friend in another town, so God sent an angel to meet him on his way. The angel approached him and asked, 'Where are you going?' The man said, 'I am visiting my brother over in that town.' The angel asked, 'Are you going so that he may repay a favor?' The man said, 'No, I am visiting only because I love him for the sake of God the Almighty.' Then the angel announced, 'I am a messenger here to tell you that God loves you as you have loved for His sake.'" *

2. Be scrupulous, even in what is allowed.

Scholars have allowed the consumption of alcohol in emergencies and situations of necessity based on the saying of the Prophet (s), "God has excused people's mistakes and forgetfulness, and also what they are forced to do." ** Even though Urwa would hold no fault or blame if he opted to consume the alcohol, he detested the idea of being in a drunken stupor for even one moment. Compare this to what most allow themselves to engage in today: hours of pointless entertainment and mindless addictions. These modern versions of "intoxicants" waste

---

*   Narrated by Muslim.
**   Sahih, narrated by Ibn Majah and Al-Hakim.

hours of the day, cause a loss in sense of time, and wither the ability to concentrate effectively. Protect and utilize time, the body, and the mind, for these are truly limited resources. Use them only in beneficial ways; "Is there anyone who will remember?" *

3. The importance of focused prayer.

Urwa's prayer far surpassed the mere recitation of words or movement of his limbs. His prayer was more than a routine obligation. Prayer is the direct connection between a person and God. It is a plea, a supplication, an act of submission and gratitude. God describes true believers as such: "Those who pray humbly." ** Urwa had achieved such intense focus in his prayer that he did not sense his own body or the people around him. His soul rose to the heavens while his body remained tethered to the earth. Who prays the prayer of Urwa, even once in a lifetime?

4. The believer is patient.

One tumultuous tragedy after another befell Urwa: a difficult journey; an illness; a painful operation; the loss of his leg; and finally, the death of his young son. Urwa's strong faith gave him the fortitude to bear these losses. He was patient, enduring intense physical pain of an amputation. Moreover, he suffered the emotional devastation of losing his child. This patience is the result of a profound understanding that everything in life happens because of God's will. Whatever loss or suffering a believer endures shall be justly compensated and generously rewarded in the Hereafter. The Prophet (s) said, "How remarkable is the situation of the believer! His situation is always good. This is the case only with the

---

*   [Al-Qamar:15]
**   [Al-Muminun:2]

believer. If he is blessed with prosperity, he is thankful and that is good for him. If he is tested with difficulty, he is patient and that is also good for him." [*]

5. Have a positive outlook on life's trials.

Urwa's wisdom led him to be content in the midst of great pain and sorrow. Urwa thanked God for His benevolence rather than complaining about the blessings he had lost. Urwa understood that there are many reasons for trials in this life - perhaps to raise a believer's status in the sight of God, or as purification from sins. The trials in life should not be automatically interpreted as revenge or punishment, but rather avenues toward mercy and the remembrance of God.

6. Difficulties become lighter with reflection.

When Urwa heard about the old man's difficulties and compared them to his own, his burdens began to feel lighter. God lessened Urwa's sorrow and eased his healing by sending him a message by virtue of the old man's tale. The account reminded Urwa that life's afflictions are like provisions, distributed among His servants according to His will. Through affliction, God distinguishes between those who are evil and those who are righteous. God says, "God will separate the bad from the good, piling the bad on top of one another, heaping them all up together, and put them in Hell. They will be the losers." [**]

---

[*]   Narrated by Muslim.
[**]   [Al-Anfal:27]

"We shall certainly test you with fear and hunger, and loss of property, lives, and crops. But give good news to those who are steadfast, those who say, when afflicted with a calamity, 'We belong to God and to Him we shall return.' These will be given blessings and mercy from their Lord, and it is they who are rightly guided."

[Al-Baqarah:155-157]

— 11 —

The Trials of Prophet Job
The Highest Example of Patience

Prophet Job, or *Ayyub* (as) *, lived prosperously in the land of *Huraan*, near what is known today as Syria. He was blessed with abundant wealth, fertile land, and cattle. Prophet Job (as) had many children, and he was surrounded by friends and relatives.

But a time came when everything suddenly changed for Prophet Job. He became so ill that his entire body was crippled. One by one, each of his children passed away. Soon, all of his possessions and money were lost as he could no longer look after his finances. As his wealth declined, so did Job's status in the community. Prophet Job became a poor, helpless man, unable to tend to his own needs.

---

*   Acronym for "*alayhi as-salat wa as-salam*" which translates to "upon him be prayers and peace." Common Islamic etiquette encourages prayers of peace to be made for the prophets at the written or spoken mention of their names.

Prophet Job's many friends and relatives eventually abandoned him. Only his wife remained strong and attentive by his side. She cared for him during his long illness, taking on odd jobs so that she could feed herself and her husband.

Prophet Job (as) suffered through sickness for eighteen long years. Despite his sorrow and poor health, he praised and thanked his Lord constantly. Job's perseverance was so great and complete that it has shone as an example throughout history as he is mentioned in God's books of revelation. Prophet Job was the epitome of patience.

Job's condition continued to worsen over eighteen years until one day he humbly pleaded to God, "Suffering has befallen me, and You are the most Merciful of the merciful." *

God answered Job immediately: "Strike the ground with your foot and wash yourself." A spring suddenly gushed from the ground, and Prophet Job cleansed himself with healing water.

Immediately, Job's weakened flesh and bones were miraculously cured. All of the pain, ruptured sores, and old scars immediately disappeared. God commanded Job to strike the earth in a different spot, and a second spring burst forth. Prophet Job drank from this water, and his internal illnesses were also washed away. He was renewed and healthy again.

When Job's wife soon met the healthy man standing in front of her, she did not recognize her husband.

She asked, " Have you seen my poor, ill husband, Prophet Job? By God, you look exactly like him when was strong and healthy!"

---

*   [Al-Anbiya:83]

Job responded to his wife, "Indeed, I am Job!"

But then the couple faced a new dilemma. At one time, when Prophet Job had been ill, his wife lost her patience and mistreated him. Job became so hurt and frustrated that he swore that if he ever regained his health, he would strike his wife one hundred times! Job's wife had helped her husband for many years without complaining, steadfast and strong. He never expected his condition to improve so that he would be bound to his oath. Now that he was healthy, Prophet Job regretted his vow and did not know how he could fulfill it.

God, in His mercy, offered Job a way out of his problem. He revealed to Prophet Job that he should use a slender blade of grass to strike his wife. He would not injure her, and at the same time he would fulfill his vow.

Prophet Job soon regained his health, wealth, friends, and social standing. He and his wife were blessed once again with many righteous children. He continued to live his life with patience, contentment, and thankfulness, just as he had done during the years of hardship. The Quran says about Job, "We found him patient in adversity; an excellent servant! He, too, always turned to God." * God finally rescued Job from adversity and recognized his character. **

*   [Saad:44]
**   Maa Al-Anbiya' fi al-Quran al-Kareem, by Afeef Abd Al-Fattah Tabbarrah, pg. 208-212.

Lessons Learned:

1. **Turn to God in all circumstances.**

   Prophet Job teaches us to seek God in every situation, good or bad. No one can relieve afflictions except for God. He brings relief, grants blessings, and controls all things. In order to turn to God, we must surrender to His will, even when we cannot understand the benefit of a given situation. God explains in the Quran, "You may dislike something although it is good for you, or like something although it is bad for you." * Only God has complete wisdom to understand the meaning of what he has ordained.

2. **Patience is one of the greatest forms of worship.**

   Prophet Job was afflicted with every imaginable calamity: he lost his health, his children, his fortune, and his position in society. Yet Job endured, not just for a few months, but for eighteen years. His relatives and friends eventually became weary and abandoned him. Job's wife stood by his side and comforted him during most of this time, but only God was able to ultimately relieve his suffering.

   Throughout these long trials, Prophet Job was mindful that every affliction was a test from God. Patience would elevate him, as the Quran promises: "We shall test you to see which of you strive your hardest and are steadfast; We shall test the sincerity of your assertions." ** Like Job, a believer should not be dismayed with any difficulty, for challenges test one's resolve and raise a believer's rank with God.

   ---
   *   [Al-Baqarah:216]
   **   [Muhammad:31]

Some people make hasty assumptions that their problems are due to God's anger. They ask, "Why me?" or "Why are others living in ease while I am in pain?" They question, "Why do we have to suffer?" Drive away these doubts and remember the certainty of God's promise. Trust in God's judgment, and be assured that for every affliction, the steadfast find relief and reward. The greatest comfort is the promise of God's recognition of those who are patient.

3. Do not despair of the mercy of God.

No matter how long or unbearable a difficulty may seem, God will send relief and ease. Patience and contentment will ease hardship and make burdens lighter to bear. Prophet Job held firm hope in God for eighteen long years. God repaid him with the restoration of his health, financial status, and society's respect. Job was even given more children to comfort him and stand by his side. For eighteen years, Job never tired of practicing patience and thankfulness. God tells us, "Do not despair of God's mercy; only disbelievers despair of God's mercy." *

4. God tests those whom He loves.

God granted Prophet Job every possible blessing: health, children, wealth, family, and social position. He was grateful for his blessings, but he understood that they were not due to his own merit. Therefore, when God took away these gifts, Job never assumed that he was entitled to them. When Prophet Job emerged from his test, he gained something even greater than his previous blessings: a refined and elevated state of patience, the rank of an "honorable servant of God," and temporal blessings which were restored and even multiplied.

---

*   [Yusuf:87]

Prophet Muhammad (s) told us, "Afflictions will continue to befall the believing man and woman, in their bodies, children, and wealth, until he and she meet God completely sinless." In times of difficulty, we must remind ourselves that trials bring us closer to God and that patience leads to Paradise. The Quran recognizes "Those who remain patient, desiring the face of their Lord; who keep up the prayer; who give secretly and openly from what We have provided for them; who repel evil with good. These will have the reward of the true home. They will enter perpetual Gardens, along with their righteous ancestors, spouses, and descendants; the angels will enter upon them from every gate, 'Peace be with you, because you have remained patient. What an excellent reward is this home of yours!'" Those who endure challenges with patience will find their reward.

5. A righteous spouse is a gift from God.

Prophet Job's wife was a model of patience and forbearance in her marriage. Her persistence rivalled that of her husband. Job's wife chose to remain by her husband's side even after losing everything: children, wealth, prestige, and the strong, dependable husband whom she had married. She chose to faithfully care for her afflicted husband, enduring all hardships alongside him.

To lose children is the greatest pain that can grieve any mother. Job's wife endured this sorrow. She also worked tirelessly to protect and nurse her husband for eighteen years. She transformed her grief and exhaustion into the praise of God, responding with a contented spirit and dedicated actions. God compensated Job's wife beyond her dreams, miraculously restoring her husband's health

---

*   Narrated by Tirmidhi.
**   [Ar-Ra'd:22-24]

and blessing her with more children. God promises, "Those who persevere patiently will be granted an unlimited reward." * The story of Job and his wife is a reminder to couples today: Be patient with life's inevitable trials, support one another through difficult times, and have a positive attitude. A great reward will surely come to the steadfast.

*   [Az-Zumar:10]

"But God only undertakes to accept repentance from those who do evil out of ignorance and soon afterwards repent: these are the ones God will forgive, He has the knowledge to decide."

[An-Nisa:17]

— 12 —
Hope for an Old Man
God Forgives Every Sin

AbdurRahman ibn Jubayr was sitting with Prophet Muhammad (s) and his companions when an old, withered man slowly made his way toward them. He walked unsteadily, using a cane, his eyebrows drooping.

Standing before the Prophet (s), the old man asked a question:

"Could you tell me about a man who has committed every possible sin, giving in to every evil whim or desire? If his sins were distributed to everyone on earth, all of them would perish because of their weighty burden. Is there any hope for this man's return to God's path?"

"Have you accepted Islam?" the Prophet asked kindly.

"Yes," the old man said, affirming that he was already a Muslim.

"Then perform good deeds and abandon your sins. God will transform all of your past actions, even your sins, into good deeds," instructed the Prophet.

"Even my deceptive and obscene behavior?" questioned the old man.

"Yes, even your deceptive and obscene behavior," confirmed Prophet Muhammad (s).

"God is great! God is great!" cried the old man. He hobbled away on his weak legs, glorifying God until he disappeared from their sight. *

*   Narrated by Ahmad, Authenticated by Al-Albani.

Lessons Learned:

1. **Acknowledging sins is the first step toward self-improvement.**

   The old man took full responsibility for his transgressions. He did not try to shift the blame for his past sins onto someone else, nor did he make excuses. Instead, he came to the Prophet (s) in all humility and weakness, taking the first step toward ridding himself of his past. His example illustrates that no matter how grave one's sins, they are like stains on white clothing: they may be removed with some effort. So do not rest until the residue of sin has been washed away, to become as pure as can be.

2. **The essential nature of humanity (fitrah) yearns to be free of sin.**

   Even though the old man was close to death, his years of sin did not prevent him from seeking a change in his final stage of life. Every person is born in fitrah, an original state of goodness and purity. This pure essence stays alive in everyone, except for those who are the absolute worst of humanity. This fitrah is weakened by sins and strengthened by good deeds. God says in the Quran, "So as one of pure faith, stand firm and true in your devotion to the religion. This is the natural disposition God instilled in mankind." * Believers must strive every day to cleanse the pure soul with which they were born, by rejecting evil practices, and making an effort to act with justice and honor.

3. **God is the Most Forgiving.**

   No matter how great one's mountain of sins, God is ready to forgive the biggest and smallest of them. As long as

---

*   [ar-Rum:30]

a believer seeks God's pleasure, he will be forgiven. The Quran says, "...My servants who have harmed yourselves by your own excess, do not despair of God's mercy. God forgives all sins: He is truly the Most Forgiving, the Most Merciful." * A believer must never lose hope. Those who sincerely seek forgiveness will find refuge in God's far-reaching mercy.

4. **Acceptance of Islam erases all past sins.**

The Prophet (s) asked the man if he had already accepted Islam because the single act of becoming Muslim automatically clears away all past sins. God says in the Quran, "God does not forgive the joining of partners with Him: anything less than that, He forgives to whomever He wills..." ** God has the power to forgive all sins, no matter how great. This mercy and generosity is open to believers once a person has entered Islam.

"If the evildoers possessed the earth's assets twice over, they would offer it to ransom themselves from the terrible suffering on the Day of Resurrection: God will show them something they had not reckoned with."

[Az-Zumar:47]

— 13 —

Revenge of the Fish

The Supplication of the Oppressed

A poor fisherman went to the river one day and cast his net into the water. He hoped to catch a fish to feed his hungry family. Hours passed, but he had not caught anything. He raised his hands, complaining to God about the cries of his famished children. Right before the sun set, a gleaming, silvery fish landed in his net.

The fisherman thanked God for his blessing and eagerly carried his catch in a bucket of water toward home to show his family. On his way, he ran into the king's entourage. When the king saw the gigantic, gleaming fish in the fisherman's possession, he wanted it for himself. The king forced the poor man to surrender his only source of food for the day.

When the king arrived at his palace, he wanted to impress the queen with the beautiful catch. He proudly brought the shining fish out to show her. The fish suddenly snapped its jaws and bit the king's finger, leaving a dreadful wound.

The king howled in pain. All night, the bite stung and throbbed from the fish's venom. The king could not sleep, and the palace doctors were summoned. They determined that the venom was spreading, and that the finger must be cut off. And so, the palace physicians reluctantly amputated the king's finger.

However, the king's pain continued. His hand burned and ached from infection as the venom continued to spread and fester. After several days, the doctors were forced to remove the king's whole hand, but still he screamed in agony. The infection spread throughout the king's entire arm. At last, after the arm was amputated, the pain finally subsided.

The king was deeply disturbed by this experience. Something troubled him in addition to the loss of his arm. Even though he no longer felt physical pain, an internal pain continued to keep him awake at night. So the king went to his wisest advisor and told him the story of the gleaming, silvery fish that he had taken from the fisherman.

The advisor said, "You will not be able to rest until the fisherman forgives you for the injustice you committed against him."

So the king searched throughout the land for the fisherman. When he found the fisherman's home, the king paid him a visit and pleaded with the poor man to forgive him. After listening politely, the fisherman assured the king that he was forgiven.

But the king had one more question: "When I took the fish from you, what words did you say to God to make this terrible punishment befall me?"

The fisherman replied, "I uttered only one sentence to my Lord: 'The king has exerted his power over me, so allow me to see You exert Your power over him.'" *

*   Anees As-Saliheen wa Sameer Al-Muttaqeen, by Muhammad AlJundi.

Lessons Learned:

1. Supplication affects provision.

The fisherman was proactive. He didn't wait in his house for his provision to find him, but rather went to the shore of the river and cast his net. He waited patiently for hours, and when that approach was unsuccessful, he pleaded for God's help. God answered him because he had done his part and exhausted all means within his capacity. Umar ibn Al-Khattab advised the Muslims, "Do not give up seeking your livelihood, saying, 'God, provide for me!' You know very well that the sky does not rain gold and silver." A believer works diligently for his needs, yet at the same time relies (*tawakkul*) completely upon God, the Provider and Sustainer.

2. Thankfulness increases wealth.

When the fisherman caught the fish, he immediately thanked the One who had given it to him. God says in the Quran, "Remember that He promised: 'If you are thankful, I will give you more, but if you are thankless, My punishment is terrible indeed.'" * In order to deserve material and spiritual blessings, thank God constantly.

3. Stealing brings misery.

When the king stole the fish, he brought misery upon himself. There are many ways to steal, so be mindful of the indirect ways of robbing the poor of their livelihood. Prophet Muhammad (s) said, "Taking from the wealth of a Muslim is forbidden, except with his or her consent." ** A believer is conscientious about what he or she consumes, making sure not to infringe upon the rights of others.

---

*   [Ibrahim:7]
**   Narrated by Al-Baihaqi and narrated by Al-Albani.

4. **Oppression will be darkness on the Day of Judgment.**

The true consequence of injustice is not in this life. The king's arm was amputated, and the pain stopped. But the king's sin continued to haunt him. If he had not atoned for his sin in this life, it would have followed him into the next life. The Prophet (s) said, "Oppression will be darkness on the Day of Judgment." [*] Taking the rights of another person brings distress to the oppressor, following him to the next life like a dark, growing storm.

5. **It is immoral to please one person by hurting another.**

The king imagined that his wife would be delighted by the fish that he brought home. This was a good intention overshadowed by injustice. The end did not justify the means. The devil may try to tempt people, encouraging them to do something evil as a means of achieving good. However, this is never a good idea and may lead to forbidden actions.

6. **Keep in mind the power of God.**

This story teaches us an important lesson: if people think that they are powerful, and able to demand whatever they want in this world, they should pause and remember the power that the Creator holds over them. Everyone should fear the supplication of a person who has been wronged, for Prophet Muhammad (s) said, "Beware of the supplication of the oppressed. It is raised above the clouds and God says, 'By My Might and Glory, I will answer you in due time.'" [**]

---

[*]   Narrated by Bukhari and Muslim.
[**]   Saheeh Al-Jami, 117.

"Do not think that God is unaware of what the disbelievers do; He only gives them respite until a Day when their eyes will stare in terror."

[Ibrahim:42]

— 14 —
The Defending Angel
Responding to Insult

Said ibn Al-Musayib, one of the companions of the Prophet (s), relayed this incident from the Prophet's life:

Once we were seated with Prophet Muhammad (s) when a man approached us and insulted Abu Bakr (ra). Abu Bakr was silent, so the man insulted him again. Abu Bakr remained quiet, so the visitor insulted him yet a third time. This time, Abu Bakr responded, silencing the man who had insulted him.

The Prophet (s) got up and left the gathering as soon as Abu Bakr responded to the man.

Abu Bakr later caught up with the Prophet and asked, "Are you upset with me, Messenger of God? Should I not have responded to the man? He kept insulting me, but I was quiet, thinking that you might respond on my behalf."

Prophet Muhammad (s) said, "There was an angel who came down from the sky just to respond on your behalf. When you finally spoke, the angel was replaced by a devil, and I did not want to remain in such company where a devil was present." *

Lessons Learned:

1. Believers are patient.

There will always be people around us who are ignorant, who have no sense and no manners. The believer is patient with these people. It is not always necessary to have the last word, and not every insult requires a response. God says in the Quran, "If you have to respond to an attack, make your response proportionate, but it is best to stand fast." * It was within Abu Bakr's right to respond to his opponent, but Prophet Muhammad (s) encouraged that we take the higher road of forbearance.

2. Forgiveness is best.

It would have been better for Abu Bakr to be patient, anticipating a reward from God. Displaying patience and forgiveness disarms attackers, causing them to pause and second guess their angry insults. God says, "Good and evil cannot be equal. Repel evil with what is better and your enemy will become as close as an old and valued friend." ** Be grateful that God has blessed you with the ability to be patient, a characteristic of the God-fearing. The Quran describes such people: "Those who give, both in prosperity and adversity, who restrain their anger and pardon people - God loves those who do good." ***

3. Revenge attracts the devil.

Retaliation for the sake of one's own ego invites the devil's company. When engaging in an argument, make sure it is for the sake of defending truth, not for self-vindication or to be proven right. When following one's own impulses in an argument, it is very easy to be transformed from

---

*   [an-Nahl:126]
**   [Fussilat:34]
***   [Aal-Imran:134]

the victim into the aggressor. The goal becomes victory over the other side, rather than the defense of truth. This kind of argument creates tension, resentment, and hatred in the community. Conversely, a principled discussion promotes goodness, critical analysis, and honest communication. Remain focused on the right goals to avoid the displeasure of God and His messenger.

4. God is the Most Patient, so be patient.

Although Abu Bakr was the best of the companions, even he could not endure repeated insults. It is nearly impossible to be patient when one is continually mistreated. Reflect upon humanity, and all of the terrible sins that are repeated again and again. God is so infinitely patient and forgiving that He can forgive all of these transgressions for those who reach out to Him. At the same time, those on earth will not live forever. It is necessary to repent to God, and it is important to be patient with others so that they too can learn about God's teachings. God says in the Quran, "If God took people to task for the evil they do He would not leave one living creature on Earth, but He reprieves them until an appointed time: when their time comes they cannot delay it for a moment nor can they bring it forward." * God gives all people time and space to reflect and come back to Him. He allows humans to experience life and see the consequences of their deeds. Praise God, who guides believers to turn back to Him before He takes their souls in death. He is the Most Patient, and he teaches believers patience to further inspire others to be among His believing servants.

---

*   [an-Nahl:61]

"Say, 'I am only a human being, like you, to whom it has been revealed that your God is One. Anyone who fears to meet his Lord should do good deeds and give no one a share in the worship due to his Lord."

[Al-Kahf:110]

— 15 —

Five Teachings of Prophet John
An Analogy for Worship

Prophet Muhammad (s) relayed this information in a hadith:

God gave Prophet John (*Yahya*) (as) five teachings. Prophet John was instructed to practice the five teachings and to convey them to the Children of Israel. However, he felt some hesitation.

Prophet Jesus (*Eesa*) (as) told John, "God gave you these five teachings and instructed you to convey them to the Children of Israel. If you are not going to command the Children of Israel to follow the teachings, then I will."

John responded, "No, I fear that if you take my place, I will be punished."

So Prophet John gathered his people in front of Al-Aqsa Mosque in Jerusalem. The mosque was overflowing with people, crowded into every corner and balcony, waiting to hear news from their prophet. Prophet John spoke as follows:

"God has given me five commandments to obey and to convey, so that you might follow them. The first is to worship God and associate no partners with Him. One who associates partners with God is like someone who pays for a very expensive servant, provides a fine home for him, and asks the servant to work for him. But instead of working for his master, the servant works for someone else. Who would want a servant like that? It is the same for someone who associates partners with God in worship: God has created you and provided for you. So do not worship other than Him.

"The second teaching is that when you stand for prayer, do not be distracted. God turns toward His servant so long as His servant does not turn away.

"The third is fasting. The fasting person is like a jar of musk, from which people enjoy a sweet aroma.

"The fourth is charity. Give in charity like someone who has been captured by the enemy, his hands chained to his throat. At the moment of his execution, the prisoner will plead for the chance to buy his own freedom. The offer is accepted, and so the prisoner will spare no amount to save himself.

"The fifth is constant remembrance of God. It is like someone who is being chased by an enemy close on his heels. The pursued man finds a huge fortress and locks himself inside before the enemy can reach him. Similarly, the servants of God will not escape from the devil unless they are protected, safe inside the fortress of the remembrance of God." *

---

*   Narrated by Tirmidhi, Authenticated by Al-Albani.

Lessons Learned:

1. Conveying the message.

From our history, we can see that God ensures that His commands have been conveyed completely and correctly to humanity. The Almighty God explains His commandments with examples and analogies that help believers grasp the meaning of His message. Prophet Jesus (*Eesa*) encouraged John to fulfill the trust God had given him without delay. God says in the Quran, "We offered the Trust to the heavens, the earth, and the mountains, yet they refused to undertake it and were afraid of it; mankind undertook it - they have always been very inept and rash." ˙ The concept of trust is very weighty in Islam - believers should be keen on fulfilling trusts in the best way, before death overtakes all.

2. The danger of associating partners with God.

There is a huge difference between the person who worships God alone and someone who associates partners in His worship. God has showered human beings with blessings, making their path through this world easier than it is for other creatures. Worshippers of God thank Him, while those who associate partners with God attribute some or all of their blessings to sources other than Him. Therefore, it is the greatest sin that a human being can commit. The Quran states, "God does not forgive the joining of partners with Him: anything less than that He forgives to whomever He wills, but anyone who joins partners with God has fabricated a tremendous sin." ˙˙

˙   [Al-Ahzab:72]
˙˙   [An-Nisa:48]

3. The importance of mindfulness in prayer.

Mindfulness in prayer is an essential component of worship, connecting servants with their Lord. Believers are commanded to nurture this connection purposefully at specific times during the course of the day. During these established times, worshippers must draw upon the powers of concentration and intentionality to make the most of the appointment. In prayer, believers call upon and confide in God, feeling the sense of powerlessness while glorifying Him. If distracted, the devil steals from these important, life-changing few minutes of the day. When Prophet Muhammad (s) was asked about the person who is distracted in prayer, he said, "It is the devil's pillage from the servant's prayer." [*] Worshippers should prepare for these precious minutes, guarding their worth.

4. The benefits of fasting.

The one who fasts is truly like a jar of perfume, filling any gathering with a sweet scent. The fasting person is extra-vigilant in avoiding lying, vain talk, and sin. Those who fast bear a radiant, calm aura during their fast. The Prophet (s) said, "God says, 'Every act of the children of Adam is for him or her, except fasting. It is for Me alone and I alone will reward it.' Fasting is a shield. When any of you is fasting, he should refrain from bad language and lower his voice; if he is insulted or provoked he should say, 'I am fasting.' By Him in Whose Hand is my soul, the breath of the fasting person is sweeter to God than the fragrance of musk. The fasting person has two joys: one when he breaks the fast and the other when he meets his Lord, pleased with his fast." [**] Fasting is a special way to draw closer to God.

---

[*]   Narrated by Bukhari.
[**]   Narrated by Muslim.

5. Charity as a protection against God's anger.

Every person commits sin and makes mistakes, so God has given believers unique ways to rectify these transgressions. Some ways to repent are spiritual: repentance; regret; calling ourselves to account. Others are verbal: seeking forgiveness; the following of cruel words with kind expressions. But the best methods of purification are action-based, of which charity is the greatest. Charity cleanses sin like flowing water. To help the needy, orphans, or the poor, whether financially or through other forms of support, charity is one of the greatest sources of reward and forgiveness. Prophet Muhammad (s) said, "Every one of you will speak to his Lord, without an intermediary. You will look to your right but see only your deeds, and look to your left and see only your deeds. You will look forward and see only Hellfire before you. Fear and avoid Hellfire at all costs, even with half of a date. If you cannot find a half-date, then with a kind word." * Remember that God loves to erase the sins of His believers, and He will accept any plea, smile, charity, or kind word. Do not procrastinate in compensating for sins now to avoid deep regret later.

6. Remembrance of God.

Enemies, whether human or in jinn form, continuously tempt the believer to forget about God. They will not rest until they have spoiled the believer's character, destroying his or her connection with Him. God urges the use of a secret weapon in fighting off these devils: the remembrance of God (*dhikr*). The Prophet (s) said, "Shall I not tell you about the best of actions, the most purifying, the greatest in status, better than gold and silver, better than striking your enemy and dying in battle?" The companions responded, "Yes, Messenger of

---

*   Agreed upon.

God!" The Prophet (s) said, "The remembrance of God." *
Wear armor - the remembrance of God - as a shield
against attacks that will arrive from the left and from the
right, attempts to divert believers from the straight path.

*   Narrated by Tirmidhi, sahih.

Other Titles by the Author

Volume 1 - Short Stories to Warm the Heart

The Virtues of Reading Quran * Live by the Verses of the Quran * Quran is Light * Quran for Healing * The Importance of Prayer (Martyrdom of 'Umar) * The Importance of Perfecting Prayer * The Importance of Friday Prayer * Reverence in Prayer * The Importance of Fajr Prayer * The Importance of Praying with a Group * Midnight Prayers * Honesty Is Your Protector * Being Truthful with the Prophet (PBUH) * The Price of Honesty * God is the Creator (Abu Hanifa and the Athiest)

Volume 2 - Kindness to Family, Supplication, and Other Short Stories to Warm the Heart

The Act of Sincerity * How Can I Be Good to My Mother? * Kindness to Parents * Dear to God, Dutiful to Parents * God Is the Merciful * God, the Giver of Life * Fasting and Higher Consciousness * The Reward for the Fasting * Supplication Is the Heart of Worship * Supplication: Relief from Distress * The Acceptance of True Supplication * The Etiquette of Eating * The Food of the Generous Is Medicine * Charity Begins at Home * The Fruits of Maintaining Bonds of Kinship

Volume 3 - Charity, Creation, and Other Short Stories to Warm the Heart

Piety and the Heart * Reaching God Through Virtuous Deeds * Consciousness of God * God is the Provider * God Is Ever-Witnessing * Belief in Judgment Day * Prosperous Charity * The Charity of Words * Charity and Growing Wealth * Shame Before God * The Best to Hire Is the Strong and Trustworthy * Arrogance, the Root of Trouble * The First Trial * The Importance of Giving Charity (Zakah) * The Recipients of Charity (Zakah)

Volume 4 - Compassion, Brotherhood, and Other Short Stories to Warm the Heart

A Lesson in Humility * The Anonymous Helper * The Mystery Worshipper * One Spoonful * 99 Murders * Catching the Fish * The Missing Finger * Marketplace Greetings * The Emperor's Rock * Rescuing a Sinner * The Story of Abraham * Sarah's Journey Through Egypt * The Pilgrimage * The Visit for God * The Loyal Friend

Volume 5 - Compassion, Brotherhood, and Other Short Stories to Warm the Heart

The Rude Neighbor * Abu Hanifa and His Neighbor * The Honest Shepherd * The Jar of Gold * Saul (Talut) the King * Ninety-Nine Sheep* Moses and Al-Khidr * A Young Scholar * Uthman Ibn Talha and Um Salamah * A Woman Cries * Amarah and the Caliph * Jabir's Camel * The Farmer in the Tree * Umar ibn Al-Khattab and the Old Woman * Ants on the Trees

Notes

Notes

Notes

Notes